Maths Revision

Helpful hints for parents

- Start at the beginning of the book and try to work through the activities in order.
- Encourage your child to work independently as much as possible, without referring to the answers!
- Discuss any areas that your child finds particularly tricky and don't worry if he or she finds any of the exercises too difficult. Remember, children learn different things at different rates.
- Give help and lots of praise, rewarding your child by adding stickers to the reward certificate for great work and effort.
- Once you have completed the workbook, move on to the practice pages bound in the centre.

Autumn Publishing

www.autumnchildrensbooks.co.uk

Addition and subtraction

Add these numbers in your head:

40 + 50 + 60 = _____   20 + 70 + 10 = _____

25 + 25 + 70 = _____   50 + 25 + 30 = _____

When adding bigger numbers it is easier to use a written method.

For example:

```
  Th H T U
     1 8 6 7
  +    2 3 5
  _____
     2 1 0 2
       1 1 1
```

remember:

Add the units first. Carry over any tens to the tens column, hundreds to the hundreds column and thousands to the thousands column.

a
```
  H T U
  5 6 2
+ 2 3 8
_____

```

b
```
  H T U
  3 8 7
+ 2 2 4
_____

```

c
```
Th H T U
 3 4 6 3
+1 9 3 9
_____

```

d
```
Th H T U
 5 8 4 6
+1 8 7 5
_____

```

e Find the total of
460 + 13 + 7 + 3402

Th H T U

+
_____

_____

f Find the total of
55 + 9 + 342 + 1348

Th H T U

+
_____

_____

Try these subtractions.

For example:

```
      Th  H   T  U
       0  13  11  1
       X   A   Z   3
   –       7   6   5
   ─────────────────
           6   5   8
```

remember:
Subtract the units first. Exchange (or borrow) from other columns if you need to, eg a ten for 10 units, a hundred for 10 tens and a thousand for 10 hundreds.

Subtract these numbers.

a
```
    H  T  U
    4  6  3
 –  1  3  9
 ──────────

```

b
```
    H  T  U
    2  3  5
 –  1  4  9
 ──────────

```

c
```
   Th H  T  U
    2  3  6  4
 –  1  8  5  7
 ─────────────

```

d
```
   Th H  T  U
    4  5  2  1
 –  1  8  7  5
 ─────────────

```

e
```
   Th H  T  U
    3  7  6  5
 –  1  9  7  5
 ─────────────

```

f
```
   Th H  T  U
    5  3  4  2
 –  1  6  9  5
 ─────────────

```

Number sequences

Count in 3s to 30

_____

Count in 6s to 60

_____

Count in 9s to 90

_____

Count in 2s to 20

_____

Count in 4s to 40

_____

Count in 8s to 80

_____

Count in 5s to 50

_____

Count in 10s to 100

_____

Count in 25s to 250

_____

Count in 50s to 500

_____

WHAT DO YOU NOTICE ABOUT THE 3s, 6s AND 9s SEQUENCES?

WHAT DO YOU NOTICE ABOUT THE 2s, 4s AND 8s SEQUENCES?

WHAT DO YOU NOTICE ABOUT THE 5s AND 10s SEQUENCES?

WHAT DO YOU NOTICE ABOUT THE 25s AND 50s SEQUENCES?

Count on from 11 in 5s

_____

Count back from 53 in 5s

_____

Count on from 10 in 9s

_____

Count back from 88 in 9s

_____

Complete this multiplication square. Then colour in the multiples of 3. What do you notice?

1	2	3	4	5	6	7	8	9	10
2	4	6	8	10		14	16		
3	6		12		18	21		27	
4		12	16	20		28	32	36	40
5		15	20					45	50
6				30	36	42	48		
7		21						63	70
8	16			40	48	56			
9	18	27	36	45	54		72	81	90
10	20	30	40	50	60	70	80	90	

remember:
Subtracting 9 is easier if you subtract 10 first, then add 1.

Complete this multiplication square. Then colour in the multiples of 4. What do you notice?

1	2	3	4	5	6	7	8	9	10
2		6	8	10		14			
3	6		12			21	24	27	
4	8							36	40
5		15	20	25	30		40		
6			24					54	60
7	14			35	42	49	56		
8				48		64	72	80	
9	18	27	36	45					90
10	20	30	40			70	80	90	

Multiplication

Multiply the numbers below using the following method.

For example: $56 \times 7 = (50 \times 7) + (6 \times 7)$

$= 350 + 42$

$= \mathbf{392}$

Now it's your turn!

a $43 \times 5 = ($ _____ $) + ($ _____ $)$

$= $ _____ $+$ _____

$= $ _____

b $28 \times 3 = ($ _____ $) + ($ _____ $)$

$= $ _____ $+$ _____

$= $ _____

c $36 \times 4 = ($ _____ $) + ($ _____ $)$

$= $ _____ $+$ _____

$= $ _____

d $69 \times 10 = ($ _____ $) + ($ _____ $)$

$= $ _____ $+$ _____

$= $ _____

Multiply the numbers below using the grid method.

For example: **52 x 36**

X	50	2	Total
30	1500	60	= 1560
6	300	12	= 312

= **1872**

Give it a go!

a 27 x 34

X			Total
			=
			=

=

b 41 x 16

X			Total
			=
			=

=

Find the answers to these long multiplications using the following methods.

For example:

```
      1  4  2
   x      2  6
   ─────────────
   2  8  4  0  (x20)
         8  5  2  (x6)
   ─────────────
   3  6  9  2
```

X	100	40	2	Total
20	2000	800	40	= 2840
6	600	240	12	= 852
				= 3692

---

a

```
      2  3  5
   x      2  5
   ─────────────
               (x20)

               (x5)
   ─────────────
```

X				Total
				=
				=
				=

---

b

```
      4  1  6
   x      2  7
   ─────────────
               (x20)

               (x7)
   ─────────────
```

X				Total
				=
				=
				=

---

c

```
      3  0  8
   x      2  4
   ─────────────
               (x20)

               (x4)
   ─────────────
```

X				Total
				=
				=
				=

---

d

```
      2  3  2
   x      3  2
   ─────────────
               (x30)

               (x2)
   ─────────────
```

X				Total
				=
				=
				=

Division

Division is the opposite of multiplication.

For example:

$7 \times 6 = 42$ **So...** $42 \div 7 = 6$ and $42 \div 6 = 7$

Write two division facts for each multiplication below.

a. $8 \times 10 =$ _____

b. $80 \times 10 =$ _____

_____

_____

_____

_____

c. $50 \times 5 =$ _____

d. $500 \times 5 =$ _____

_____

_____

_____

_____

Dividing long numbers in your head is difficult so you need to learn a written method.

For example:

```
          3  4 r 1
    6 | 2  0  5
    -   1  8      (6 x 3)
           2  5
    -      2  4   (6 x 4)
              1
```

'R' MEANS REMAINDER!

remember:
Division is also like repeated subtraction.
E.g. $42 \div 6 = 42 - 6 - 6 - 6 - 6 - 6 - 6 - 6$

a

b

c

d

e

```
5 | 4  5  7
```

```
3 | 6  0  4
```

```
2 | 1  5  6
```

```
8 | 3  4  7
```

```
4 | 5  2  0
```

Always try to estimate your answers first when you are dividing.

For example: **300 ÷ 9**

You know that 300 ÷ 10 = 30 so you can estimate that 300 ÷ 9 will be a bit more than 30.

Now do the division to find out the answer …

```
           3   3  r 3
      9 │ 3  0  0
       -  2  7    (3 x 9)
          3  0
       -     2  7  (3 x 9)
              3
```

Work out these division problems.

Estimate your answers first.

1. Share £11.50 equally between Sam and Pam.

2. 720 divided by 3.

3. How many 150 cm ribbons can you make from 600 cm?

4. 696 ÷ 6

5. Share 2060 by 20.

6. How many groups of 8 are there in 448?

Do your working out here…

Rounding numbers

When making rough estimates in your head, rounding numbers (up or down) is useful.

For example, numbers from 101 to 104 can be rounded down to 100 and from 105 to 109 rounded up to 110.

Round these numbers to the nearest ten.

a. 21 _____

b. 687 _____

c. 453 _____

d. 999 _____

Decimals

A **decimal** is part of a whole number. It is similar to a fraction.

0.5 is the same as ½

1.5 is the same as 1½

We say:

0.5 = nought point five

1.5 = one point five

remember:
The number before the decimal point is a whole number. The number after the decimal point is a part of a whole number.

Write these decimals on the number line.

0.2   0.5   1.3   1.5   1.9   0.7   1.1   0.8

0   1   2

Write these numbers in order from the smallest to the biggest.

a. 7.3, 6.5, 9.2, 5.1

_____ _____ _____ _____

b. 96p, £1.06, £96, £1.96

_____ _____ _____ _____

c. 0.5 cm, 1.5 cm, 2.5 cm, 1.2 cm

_____ _____ _____ _____

d. 5.2 m, 5.5 m, 5.1 m, 5.9 m

_____ _____ _____ _____

MONEY IS WRITTEN IN DECIMALS – SO IT'S WORTH YOUR WHILE GETTING TO KNOW THEM!

Money and other measures, such as length, weight and volume, use decimals.

For example:

100 cm = 1 m   1000 g = 1 kg   1000 ml = 1 litre

150 cm = 1.5 m   1100 g = 1.1 kg   1900 ml = 1.9 litres

Find out:

a. How many pence in £2.50? _____ p

b. What is 673p in pounds and pence? £ _____

c. How many centimetres in 1.10 metres? _____ cm

d. What is 350 cm written in metres? _____ m

e. What comes next? 5.0, 5.2, 5.4, _____ , _____

f. What comes next? 7.1, 6.9, 6.7, _____ , _____

g. What is 1400 g in kilograms? _____ kg

h. How many millilitres in 1.4 litres? _____ ml

Decimals have fraction equivalents.

For example:

$0.50 = \dfrac{1}{2}$ $0.25 = \dfrac{1}{4}$ $0.20 = \dfrac{1}{5}$ $0.1 = \dfrac{1}{10}$ $0.01 = \dfrac{1}{100}$

PUT THESE FRACTIONS IN A CALCULATOR TO CHECK THE DECIMAL EQUIVALENTS.

remember:

0.50 is the same as 0.5

In money, 0.5 would be worth 50p.

0.05 would be 5p.

Draw a line to join each decimal to its fraction equivalent.

0.20	0.02	0.60	0.75	0.35	0.10

$\dfrac{75}{100}$	$\dfrac{35}{100}$	$\dfrac{20}{100}$	$\dfrac{2}{100}$	$\dfrac{10}{100}$	$\dfrac{60}{100}$

Fractions

A **fraction** is a part of a whole.

If we halve something, we divide it into two equal parts.

We write this as: $\frac{1}{2}$

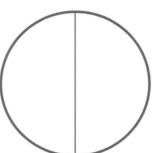

Colour these fractions of the shapes.

1 Colour $\frac{1}{2}$

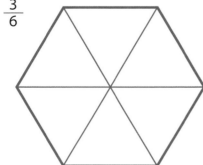

2 Colour $\frac{2}{3}$

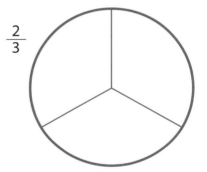

3 Colour $\frac{2}{4}$

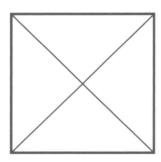

4 Colour $\frac{4}{5}$

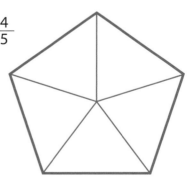

5 Colour $\frac{3}{6}$

$\frac{2}{4}$ AND $\frac{3}{6}$ ARE THE SAME AS $\frac{1}{2}$!!

Fractions that have the same value are called **equivalent fractions**.

For example:

$\frac{1}{2}$ is the same as $\frac{4}{8}$, $\frac{5}{10}$, $\frac{6}{12}$ and $\frac{50}{100}$ etc.

Can you think of any other equivalent fractions? Write them in the space below.

Draw a ring around the fractions that are less than $\frac{1}{2}$.

$\frac{6}{14}$ $\frac{3}{8}$ $\frac{5}{10}$ $\frac{9}{20}$ $\frac{60}{100}$ $\frac{7}{16}$ $\frac{9}{12}$

Draw a ring around the fractions that are more than $\frac{1}{2}$.

$\frac{12}{20}$ $\frac{7}{12}$ $\frac{4}{8}$ $\frac{9}{16}$ $\frac{6}{18}$ $\frac{6}{10}$ $\frac{8}{24}$

Write these fractions in order from the smallest.

$\frac{1}{5}$ $\frac{3}{4}$ $\frac{1}{10}$ $\frac{3}{6}$

___   ___   ___   ___

What fraction of this shape is coloured?

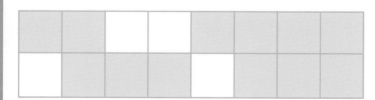

remember:
You can simplify a fraction by dividing the top number and the bottom number by the same factor.

eg $\frac{12}{16}$ (÷ by 4) = $\frac{3}{4}$

Shapes

Name these shapes.

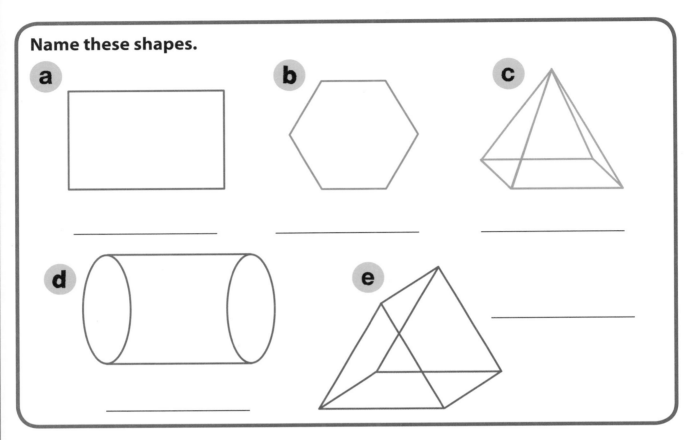

a

b

c

d

e

Complete the following statement.

A cube has:

_____ faces.

_____ edges.

_____ corners (vertices).

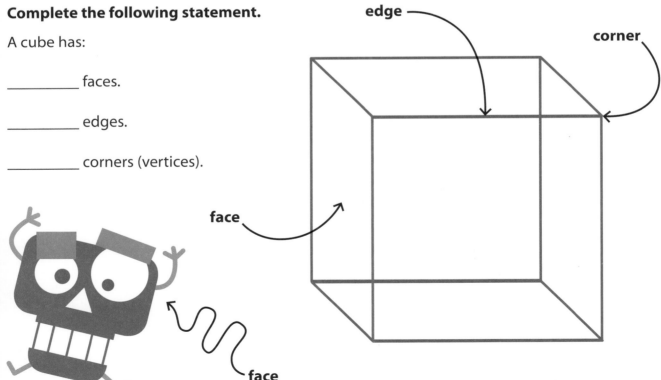

edge

corner

face

face

ADDITION AND SUBTRACTION

Add and subtract these numbers.

a.
```
  H T U
    4 5
+ 2 5 4
───────

───────
```

b.
```
  H T U
  9 7 5
+   3 1
───────

───────
```

c.
```
  H T U
  3 2 4
+ 5 6 4
───────

───────
```

d.
```
Th H T U
 6 0 2 2
-1 0 4 3
────────

────────
```

e.
```
Th H T U
 7 0 3 5
-5 0 6 6
────────

────────
```

f.
```
Th H T U
 6 3 3 1
-2 0 0 1
────────

────────
```

Find the total of:

g. $24 + 450 + 3 =$ _____

h. $52 + 607 + 33 =$ _____

i. $9 + 22 + 42 + 90 =$ _____

j. $453 + 67 + 900 =$ _____

k. $760 + 3452 + 40 =$ _____

l. $5671 + 462 + 12 + 50 =$ _____

m. $77 + 112 + 9388 =$ _____

n. $560 - 14 - 3 =$ _____

o. $8992 - 549 =$ _____

PERIMETER AND AREA

Find the perimeter of these shapes.

a Perimeter = _____ cm

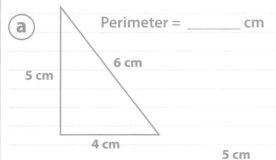

6 cm

5 cm

4 cm

b

9 cm

4 cm

Perimeter = _____ cm

c Perimeter = _____ cm

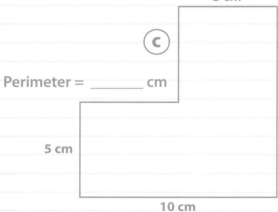

5 cm

5 cm

10 cm

d

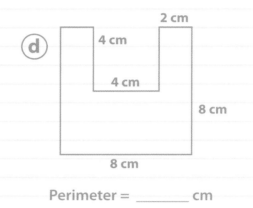

2 cm

4 cm

4 cm

8 cm

8 cm

Perimeter = _____ cm

Find the area of these shapes.

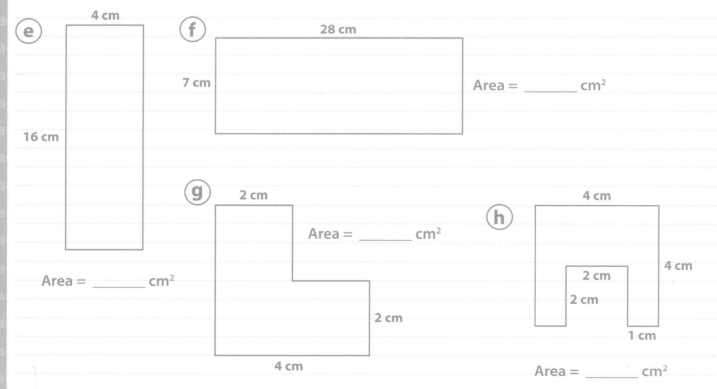

e 4 cm

16 cm

Area = _____ cm²

f 28 cm

7 cm

Area = _____ cm²

g 2 cm

Area = _____ cm²

2 cm

4 cm

h 4 cm

4 cm

2 cm

2 cm

1 cm

Area = _____ cm²

ANGLES AND TRIANGLES

Work out the missing angles in these triangles.

a
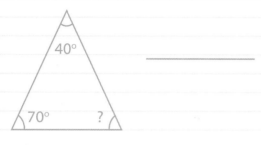
_____

b

_____

c
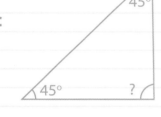
_____

d
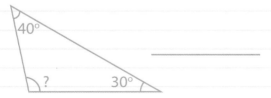
_____

Write the names of these types of triangles.

e
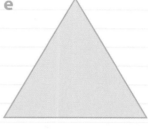
_____

f

_____

g
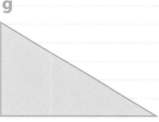
_____

h
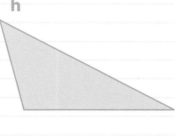
_____

DIVISION

Answer these division sums.

a. $72 \div 8 = \boxed{}$

b. $45 \div 9 = \boxed{}$

c. $36 \div \boxed{} = 6$

d. $\boxed{} \div 7 = 11$

e. $\boxed{} \div 8 = 8$

f. $81 \div 9 = \boxed{}$

g. $\boxed{} \div 9 = 2$

h. $35 \div \boxed{} = 5$

i. $32 \div 8 = \boxed{}$

j. $100 \div 10 = \boxed{}$

k. $\boxed{} \div 3 = 7$

l. $12 \div 4 = \boxed{}$

m. $55 \div \boxed{} = 11$

n. $27 \div \boxed{} = 9$

o. $15 \div 5 = \boxed{}$

p. $99 \div \boxed{} = 11$

q. $10 \div \boxed{} = 2$

r. $\boxed{} \div 4 = 4$

s. $\boxed{} \div 3 = 3$

t. $20 \div 4 = \boxed{}$

Write true (T) or false (F) next to each of these statements.

1. A triangle has 3 sides. ☐

2. A cuboid has 8 faces. ☐

3. A cylinder has 1 face. ☐

4. A cylinder has 2 edges. ☐

5. A triangular prism has 9 edges. ☐

6. A square has 4 equal sides. ☐

7. A pentagon has 6 sides. ☐

Draw lines of symmetry on these shapes.

remember:

Some shapes have more than one line of symmetry.

Angles

An **angle** is a rotation around a point. We measure angles in **degrees** using a protractor.

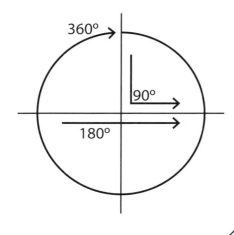

360 degrees = a circle

180 degrees = a straight line

90 degrees = a quarter-turn (a right angle)

An angle **less** than 90 degrees is called **acute**.

An angle **more** than 90 degrees is called **obtuse**.

Label these angles 'acute' or 'obtuse'.

  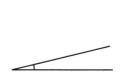 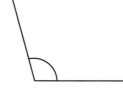

a _____

b _____

c _____

d _____

Calculate the unknown angle.

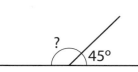 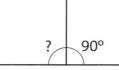  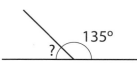

a _____

b _____

c _____

d _____

The angles in a triangle add up to 180 degrees.

60°

60°   60°

remember:

If you know two of the angles in a triangle you can calculate the third angle by subtracting from 180.

a
?

70°   70°

_____

b
?

60°   60°

_____

c
?

45°   90°

_____

d
?

100°   40°

_____

There are different types of triangle:

equilateral – 3 equal sides, 3 equal angles

isosceles – 2 equal sides, 2 equal angles

scalene – no equal sides, no equal angles

right-angled – one right angle

Identify these triangles using the definitions above.

a

b

c

_____   _____   _____

d

_____

remember:

A right-angled triangle is labelled like this:

Area and perimeter

Area is a measurement of the space inside a shape.

If each square represents 1 square cm, what area is shaded?

_____ cm²

Perimeter is the distance around the edges of a shape.

What is the perimeter of the shape above? _____ cm

Draw your own shape in this space and find out its perimeter and area.

Find the area and perimeter of these shapes.

For example:

6 cm

2 cm

area = 2 x 6 = 12 cm²

perimeter = 2 + 2 + 6 + 6 = 16 cm

a

14 cm

10 cm

area = _____ cm²

perimeter = _____ cm

b

20 cm

4 cm

area = _____ cm²

perimeter = _____ cm

c

15 cm

7 cm

area = _____ cm²

perimeter = _____ cm

d

10 cm

30 cm

area = _____ cm²

perimeter = _____ cm

What is the approximate area of this rectangle?

Round the decimals down or up to find out.

12.4 cm

19.7 cm

approximate area = _____ cm²

Negative numbers

Complete this temperature scale.

Use the number line to do these subtractions by counting back.

a. - 4 – 6 = ____

b. - 3 – 5 = ____

c. -1 – 4 = ____

d. 6 – 8 = ____

e. 2 – 5 = ____

f. 3 – 6 = ____

g. - 5 – 5 = ____

h. 9 – 17 = ____

i. 6 – 12 = ____

j. 2 – 10 = ____

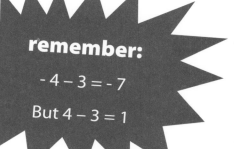

remember:

- 4 – 3 = - 7

But 4 – 3 = 1

Percentages

A **percentage** is a part of a hundred.

Revise these percentage and fraction equivalents:

$1\% = \frac{1}{100}$ (one-hundredth)

$10\% = \frac{10}{100}$ (one-tenth)

$25\% = \frac{25}{100}$ (one-quarter)

$50\% = \frac{50}{100}$ (half)

What percentage of each shape is shaded?

 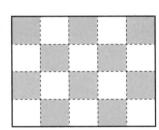

 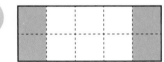

Now try these!

a. 50% of 100 = _____

b. 50% of 40 = _____

c. 25% of £1 = _____p

d. 10% of £1 = _____p

e. 10% of 50p = _____p

f. $\frac{1}{4}$ of 80 cm = _____cm

g. 25% of 1 kg = _____g

h. $\frac{1}{10}$ of 30 ml = _____ml

Colour in 75% of each shape.

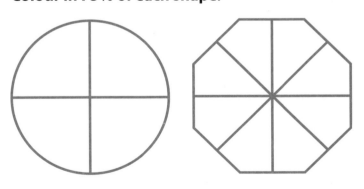

remember:
$75\% = 50\% + 25\%$ or $\frac{1}{2} + \frac{1}{4}$

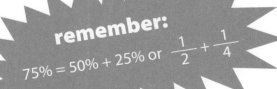

Graphs

Look at the bar graph that shows the height of children in Class 6.

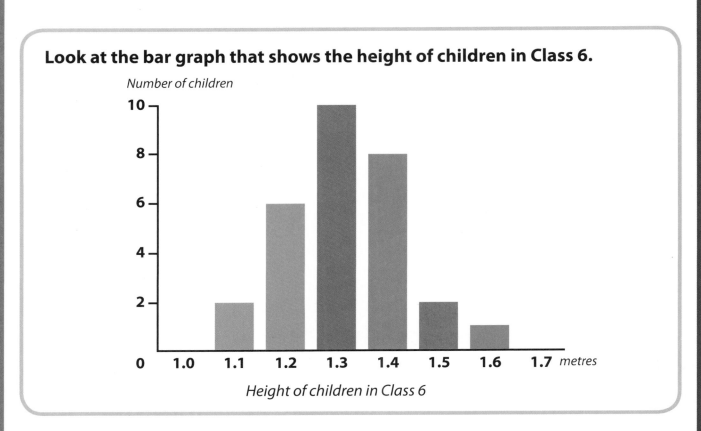

Number of children

Height of children in Class 6

Answer the following questions based on the graph.

a. Which is the most common height for children in Class 6? _____ m

b. What is 1.2 m in centimetres? _____ cm

c. What height are the shortest children in the class? _____ cm

d. What is the difference in height between the shortest and the tallest child? _____ cm

e. How many children are in Class 6? _____ children

WHO'S TALLER?

Look at the pie chart that shows the children's eye colours in Class 7.

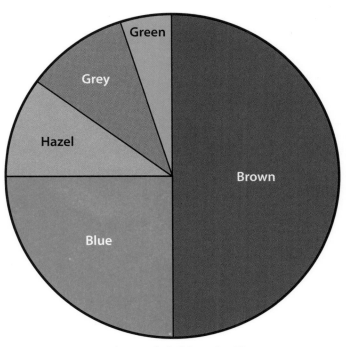

Eye colour of children in Class 7

There are 20 children in Class 7.

Answer the following questions based on the pie chart.

a. Which is the most common eye colour? _____

b. Which is the least common eye colour? _____

c. How many children have grey eyes? _____

d. What percentage of children have brown eyes? _____%

e. What percentage of children have blue eyes? _____%

LOOK INTO MY EYE!

Coordinates

Coordinates are the numbers we use to pinpoint a place on a graph or map.

Look at the map below. You will find Skull Rock at (4, 5). Write the coordinates for the following:

a. Creepy cave (__ , __)

b. Stinky swamp (__ , __)

c. Skull and crossbones (__ , __)

d. Buried treasure (__ , __)

remember:
First you read along the x axis, then the y axis.

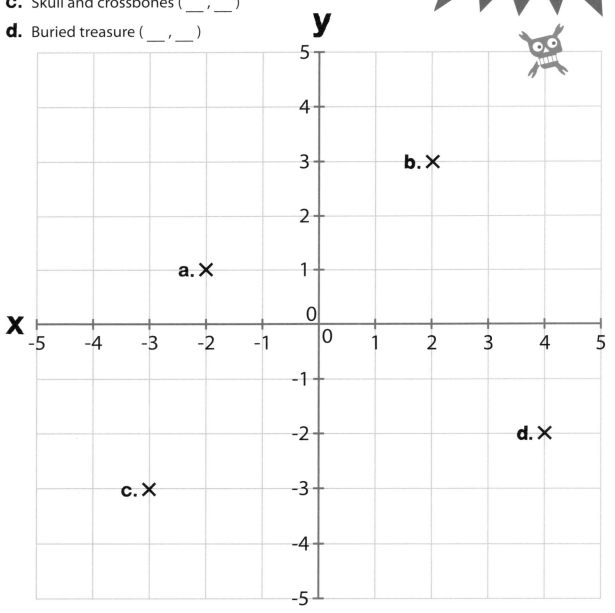

Draw your own treasure map with buried treasure.

Write the coordinates of the buried treasure here: (__ , __)

Write the coordinates for three other important places on your map.

Place name: _____ (__ , __)

Place name: _____ (__ , __)

Place name: _____ (__ , __)

y

5

4

3

2

1

0

x

-5 -4 -3 -2 -1   0   1   2   3   4   5

-1

-2

-3

-4

-5

Puzzles

1. Count all the squares you can find in this shape.

2. Complete this number sudoku so that each 3 x 2 block includes all the numbers from 1 to 6. The columns and rows must also include all these numbers.

3				1	4
	1	6			
	6	4	5		3
		2	4	6	1
6			3		
2	5				6

3. Complete these multiplication tables.

X	7	4	2	Total
3	21			= 39
	42			=
		32		=
5				=

X	6		9	Total
	36			=
7		70		=
			27	=
	30			=

4. Write the factors for each number on these spider diagrams.

a
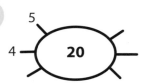
5
4
20

b
24

c

21

d
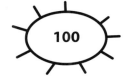
100

remember:
A **factor** is a number that will divide evenly (without a remainder) into another number, eg 3, 9 and 1 are factors of 9.

5. A short dog lead is 100 cm long. A long lead is 2 m. How much longer is the long lead in centimetres? _____ cm